Mental Maths Every Day for ages 5–6

Dear Parents,

Thank you for buying this copy of *Mental Maths Every Day 5–6*, one of a six book series of maths practice books for primary aged children.

Why is mental maths so important?
All children need to know number facts so that they can remember them instantly when working on more complex aspects of maths. Children who are confident in mental maths also tend to be more confident when faced with money, time, measurements and other mathematical concepts.

This book is designed to boost children's confidence by giving them plenty of practice in quick calculations. The calculations become progressively more difficult as the child works through the book. Don't be surprised if the first few pages seem easy – it's still important that your child completes them. Your child will find some of the other pages very difficult but this is quite normal too; just be on hand to provide help and guidance when needed.

How do I use the book?
Each page of this book is split into columns of questions that have been specially devised for children aged 5–6. Using a stopwatch or clock, ask your child to do as many questions as possible from the first column in exactly one minute. Allow your child to use fingers or counters if she/he needs to. Prompt your child to look very carefully at each question, paying special attention to the mathematical symbol – for example, whether it is an instruction to add or subtract.

At the end of the minute, mark the questions with your child and write down the score for the column in the score box. To save time, the answers are provided on pages 30 to 32. Your child probably won't have time to complete all the questions in the column but praise her/him for trying hard and doing as many as possible. Take the opportunity to discuss any mistakes that have been made and show the child how to do any questions that have been missed out. When she/he is ready your child can complete the next column and try and improve the score. Don't worry if it doesn't improve immediately – 'practice makes perfect' and the improvement in performance will take place sooner or later. Remember that the best way to help is to give lots of praise for success and lots of support where the child is experiencing any difficulty. I do hope that your child enjoys working through the activities.

Andrew Brodie

Contents

Adding 1 to numbers up to 10

See if you can answer each set of 10 questions in one minute.

4 + 1 =			
7 + 1 =			
2 + 1 =			
5 + 1 =			
0 + 1 =			
9 + 1 =			
6 + 1 =			
1 + 1 =			
8 + 1 =			
3 + 1 =			

Score

5 + 1 =			
2 + 1 =			
7 + 1 =			
6 + 1 =			
1 + 1 =			
3 + 1 =			
8 + 1 =			
4 + 1 =			
0 + 1 =			
9 + 1 =			

Score

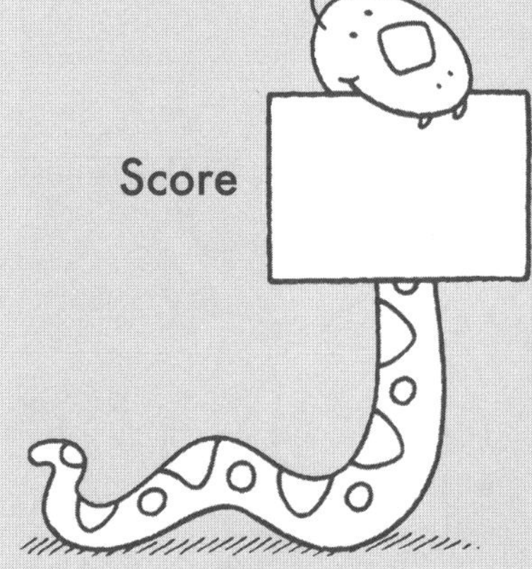

7 + 1 =			
0 + 1 =			
1 + 1 =			
6 + 1 =			
3 + 1 =			
8 + 1 =			
4 + 1 =			
9 + 1 =			
2 + 1 =			
5 + 1 =			

Score

For answers see page 30

Subtracting 1 from numbers up to 10

See if you can answer each set of 10 questions in one minute.

7 - 1 = ☐	3 - 1 = ☐	10 - 1 = ☐
4 - 1 = ☐	7 - 1 = ☐	5 - 1 = ☐
9 - 1 = ☐	1 - 1 = ☐	2 - 1 = ☐
6 - 1 = ☐	5 - 1 = ☐	7 - 1 = ☐
5 - 1 = ☐	8 - 1 = ☐	8 - 1 = ☐
2 - 1 = ☐	10 - 1 = ☐	3 - 1 = ☐
10 - 1 = ☐	4 - 1 = ☐	6 - 1 = ☐
3 - 1 = ☐	6 - 1 = ☐	1 - 1 = ☐
1 - 1 = ☐	2 - 1 = ☐	4 - 1 = ☐
8 - 1 = ☐	9 - 1 = ☐	9 - 1 = ☐
Score ☐	Score ☐	Score ☐

For answers see page 30

Adding and subtracting 1 from numbers up to 10

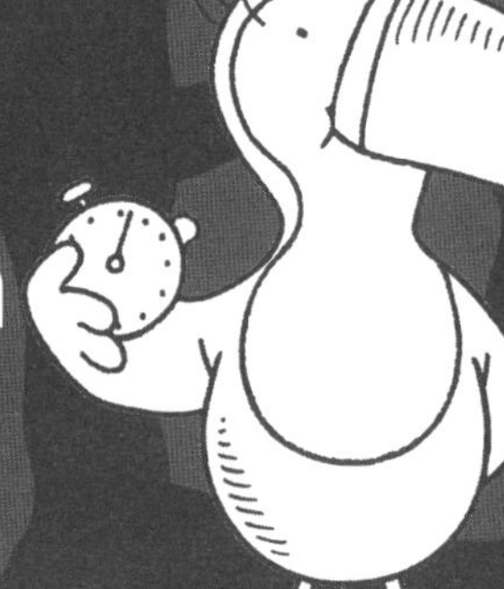

5 + 1 = ☐	2 + 1 = ☐	6 + 1 = ☐
6 - 1 = ☐	5 - 1 = ☐	3 - 1 = ☐
3 + 1 = ☐	4 + 1 = ☐	8 + 1 = ☐
3 - 1 = ☐	8 - 1 = ☐	4 - 1 = ☐
8 + 1 = ☐	6 + 1 = ☐	1 + 1 = ☐
6 + 1 = ☐	3 - 1 = ☐	9 - 1 = ☐
2 - 1 = ☐	1 + 1 = ☐	5 + 1 = ☐
4 + 1 = ☐	7 - 1 = ☐	6 - 1 = ☐
7 - 1 = ☐	5 + 1 = ☐	2 + 1 = ☐
9 + 1 = ☐	9 - 1 = ☐	7 - 1 = ☐
Score ☐	Score ☐	Score ☐

For answers see page 30

Adding 1 to numbers up to 20

See if you can answer each set of 10 questions in one minute.

12 + 1 =	17 + 1 =	10 + 1 =
16 + 1 =	14 + 1 =	15 + 1 =
15 + 1 =	16 + 1 =	17 + 1 =
19 + 1 =	19 + 1 =	13 + 1 =
10 + 1 =	8 + 1 =	18 + 1 =
13 + 1 =	15 + 1 =	7 + 1 =
17 + 1 =	11 + 1 =	12 + 1 =
9 + 1 =	13 + 1 =	16 + 1 =
14 + 1 =	18 + 1 =	11 + 1 =
11 + 1 =	12 + 1 =	14 + 1 =

Score

Score

Score

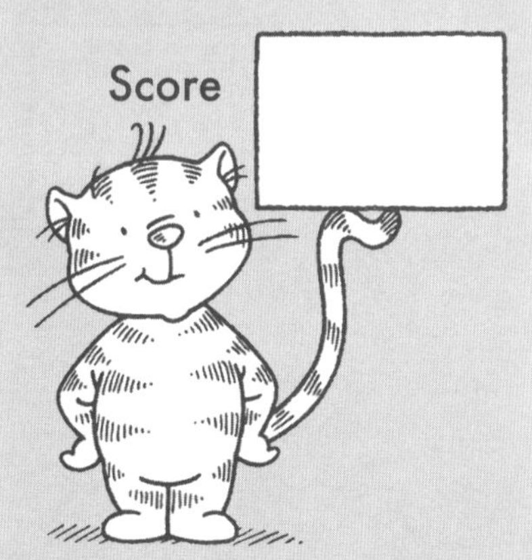

For answers see page 30

Subtracting 1 from numbers up to 20

See if you can answer each set of 10 questions in one minute.

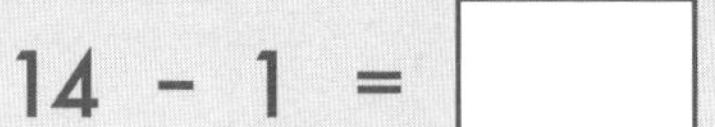

14 - 1 =	18 - 1 =	13 - 1 =
17 - 1 =	14 - 1 =	17 - 1 =
10 - 1 =	17 - 1 =	12 - 1 =
15 - 1 =	11 - 1 =	19 - 1 =
19 - 1 =	16 - 1 =	11 - 1 =
12 - 1 =	19 - 1 =	10 - 1 =
18 - 1 =	10 - 1 =	14 - 1 =
16 - 1 =	20 - 1 =	18 - 1 =
13 - 1 =	12 - 1 =	20 - 1 =
11 - 1 =	15 - 1 =	15 - 1 =

Score

Score

Score

Adding and subtracting 1 up to 20

See if you can answer each set of 10 questions in one minute.

13 + 1 =

15 - 1 =

18 + 1 =

12 - 1 =

14 + 1 =

19 - 1 =

17 + 1 =

10 - 1 =

16 + 1 =

11 - 1 =

Score

14 - 1 =

13 + 1 =

19 - 1 =

11 + 1 =

17 - 1 =

15 + 1 =

12 - 1 =

16 + 1 =

18 - 1 =

10 + 1 =

Score

16 + 1 =

17 - 1 =

13 + 1 =

19 - 1 =

10 + 1 =

12 - 1 =

15 + 1 =

11 - 1 =

18 + 1 =

14 - 1 =

Score

For answers see page 30

Adding 1 to numbers up to 100

39 + 1 = ☐	62 + 1 = ☐	75 + 1 = ☐
65 + 1 = ☐	29 + 1 = ☐	49 + 1 = ☐
42 + 1 = ☐	84 + 1 = ☐	32 + 1 = ☐
81 + 1 = ☐	30 + 1 = ☐	96 + 1 = ☐
58 + 1 = ☐	78 + 1 = ☐	21 + 1 = ☐
60 + 1 = ☐	52 + 1 = ☐	65 + 1 = ☐
74 + 1 = ☐	45 + 1 = ☐	57 + 1 = ☐
22 + 1 = ☐	73 + 1 = ☐	89 + 1 = ☐
37 + 1 = ☐	98 + 1 = ☐	36 + 1 = ☐
51 + 1 = ☐	83 + 1 = ☐	51 + 1 = ☐

Score ☐

Score ☐

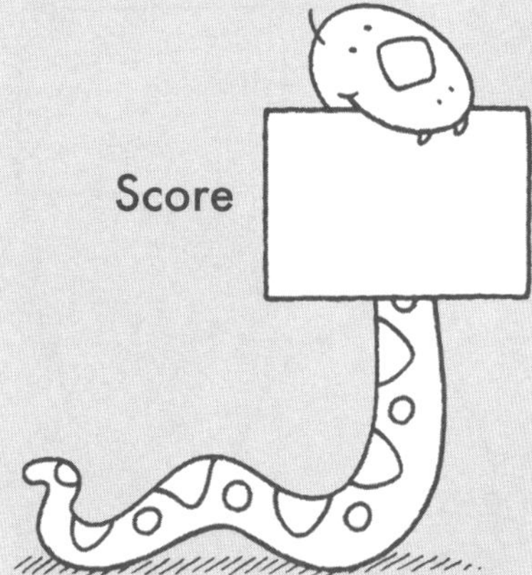

Score ☐

For answers see page 30

Subtracting 1 from numbers up to 100

See if you can answer each set of 10 questions in one minute.

60 - 1 = ☐
35 - 1 = ☐
78 - 1 = ☐
22 - 1 = ☐
49 - 1 = ☐
83 - 1 = ☐
54 - 1 = ☐
92 - 1 = ☐
34 - 1 = ☐
79 - 1 = ☐

Score ☐

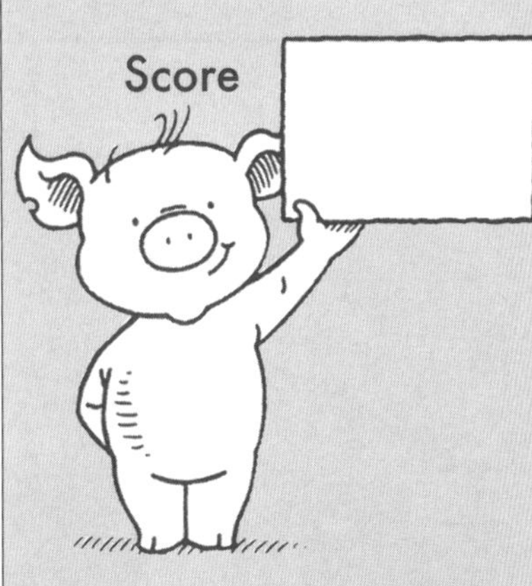

45 - 1 = ☐
52 - 1 = ☐
93 - 1 = ☐
71 - 1 = ☐
30 - 1 = ☐
89 - 1 = ☐
44 - 1 = ☐
28 - 1 = ☐
66 - 1 = ☐
87 - 1 = ☐

Score ☐

56 - 1 = ☐
94 - 1 = ☐
20 - 1 = ☐
45 - 1 = ☐
37 - 1 = ☐
65 - 1 = ☐
73 - 1 = ☐
29 - 1 = ☐
88 - 1 = ☐
70 - 1 = ☐

Score ☐

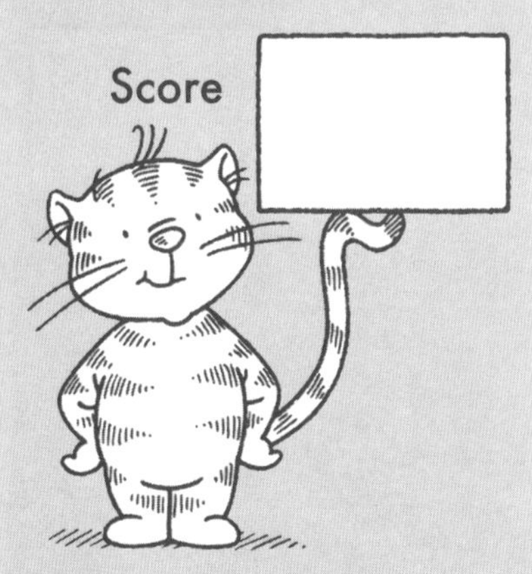

For answers see page 30

Adding and subtracting 1 up to 100

See if you can answer each set of 10 questions in one minute.

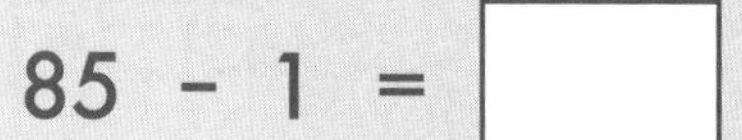

85 - 1 =

76 + 1 =

23 - 1 =

54 + 1 =

37 - 1 =

82 + 1 =

98 - 1 =

41 + 1 =

10 - 1 =

69 + 1 =

Score

45 + 1 =

82 - 1 =

66 - 1 =

23 + 1 =

73 - 1 =

81 + 1 =

97 - 1 =

89 + 1 =

38 - 1 =

54 + 1 =

Score

71 + 1 =

29 - 1 =

57 + 1 =

40 - 1 =

84 + 1 =

62 - 1 =

19 + 1 =

36 - 1 =

93 + 1 =

54 - 1 =

Score

For answers see page 30

Addition facts up to 10

See if you can answer each set of 10 questions in one minute.

6 + 3 = ☐
2 + 8 = ☐
1 + 4 = ☐
5 + 2 = ☐
7 + 1 = ☐
3 + 6 = ☐
4 + 5 = ☐
3 + 3 = ☐
5 + 4 = ☐
1 + 6 = ☐

Score ☐

6 + 2 = ☐
7 + 1 = ☐
3 + 4 = ☐
1 + 8 = ☐
6 + 4 = ☐
7 + 2 = ☐
3 + 5 = ☐
2 + 4 = ☐
5 + 2 = ☐
8 + 2 = ☐

Score ☐

7 + 2 = ☐
9 + 1 = ☐
5 + 3 = ☐
8 + 2 = ☐
6 + 4 = ☐
3 + 6 = ☐
2 + 5 = ☐
6 + 1 = ☐
5 + 5 = ☐
4 + 3 = ☐

Score ☐

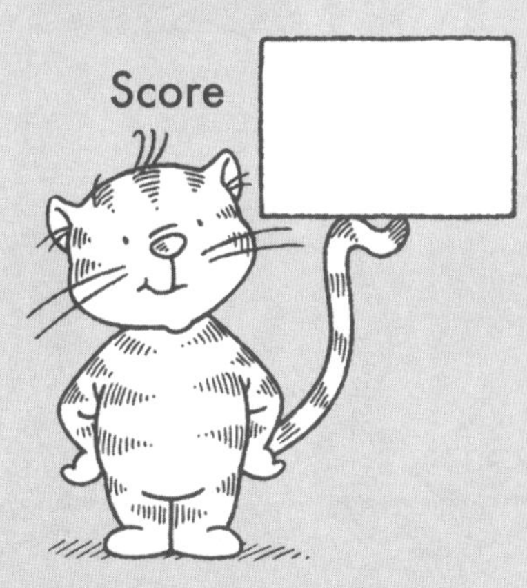

For answers see page 31

Subtraction facts up to 10

See if you can answer each set of 10 questions in one minute.

9 - 4 = ☐
5 - 2 = ☐
8 - 3 = ☐
8 - 6 = ☐
4 - 2 = ☐
9 - 6 = ☐
5 - 3 = ☐
7 - 6 = ☐
5 - 4 = ☐
8 - 5 = ☐

Score ☐

6 - 4 = ☐
7 - 2 = ☐
8 - 4 = ☐
2 - 2 = ☐
6 - 5 = ☐
3 - 2 = ☐
8 - 5 = ☐
4 - 3 = ☐
6 - 3 = ☐
4 - 4 = ☐

Score ☐

7 - 4 = ☐
3 - 3 = ☐
4 - 3 = ☐
8 - 7 = ☐
6 - 2 = ☐
2 - 1 = ☐
8 - 6 = ☐
5 - 4 = ☐
7 - 3 = ☐
4 - 2 = ☐

Score ☐

For answers see page 31

Addition and subtraction facts up to 10

See if you can answer each set of 10 questions in one minute.

5 + 3 = ☐	6 - 4 = ☐	4 + 3 = ☐
7 - 5 = ☐	2 + 7 = ☐	8 - 5 = ☐
2 + 6 = ☐	7 - 3 = ☐	2 + 6 = ☐
4 - 3 = ☐	5 + 4 = ☐	6 - 4 = ☐
9 + 1 = ☐	3 - 1 = ☐	5 + 5 = ☐
3 - 3 = ☐	5 + 2 = ☐	5 - 4 = ☐
6 + 2 = ☐	8 - 6 = ☐	2 + 7 = ☐
8 - 6 = ☐	4 + 3 = ☐	4 - 4 = ☐
2 + 7 = ☐	7 - 6 = ☐	8 + 1 = ☐
4 - 2 = ☐	6 + 4 = ☐	5 - 3 = ☐
Score ☐	Score ☐	Score ☐

For answers see page 31

Subtracting from 10

10 - 4 =	10 - 8 =	10 - 3 =
10 - 5 =	10 - 3 =	10 - 7 =
10 - 3 =	10 - 5 =	10 - 2 =
10 - 8 =	10 - 1 =	10 - 6 =
10 - 1 =	10 - 4 =	10 - 5 =
10 - 7 =	10 - 9 =	10 - 8 =
10 - 2 =	10 - 6 =	10 - 4 =
10 - 3 =	10 - 7 =	10 - 1 =
10 - 6 =	10 - 2 =	10 - 9 =
10 - 9 =	10 - 8 =	10 - 7 =

Score

Score

Score

For answers see page 31

Addition facts up to 20

See if you can answer each set of 10 questions in one minute.

8 + 7 = ☐
4 + 8 = ☐
3 + 7 = ☐
2 + 9 = ☐
5 + 9 = ☐
3 + 5 = ☐
4 + 5 = ☐
1 + 8 = ☐
6 + 7 = ☐
9 + 6 = ☐

Score

2 + 6 = ☐
4 + 9 = ☐
3 + 8 = ☐
6 + 8 = ☐
1 + 7 = ☐
2 + 8 = ☐
7 + 9 = ☐
4 + 7 = ☐
8 + 4 = ☐
5 + 2 = ☐

Score

6 + 8 = ☐
7 + 4 = ☐
6 + 3 = ☐
8 + 3 = ☐
5 + 9 = ☐
3 + 8 = ☐
5 + 6 = ☐
4 + 9 = ☐
9 + 4 = ☐
5 + 9 = ☐

Score

For answers see page 31

Subtraction facts up to 20

See if you can answer each set of 10 questions in one minute.

16 - 9 = ☐
18 - 5 = ☐
11 - 4 = ☐
13 - 7 = ☐
18 - 5 = ☐
19 - 4 = ☐
15 - 5 = ☐
18 - 6 = ☐
12 - 7 = ☐
14 - 8 = ☐

Score ☐

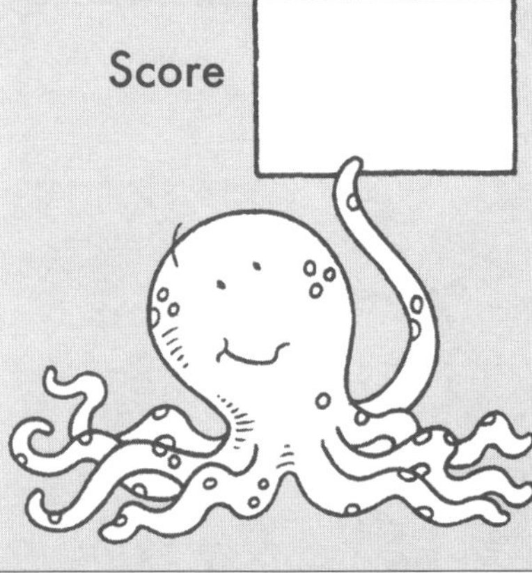

17 - 5 = ☐
12 - 6 = ☐
19 - 3 = ☐
14 - 6 = ☐
16 - 2 = ☐
18 - 7 = ☐
11 - 5 = ☐
12 - 3 = ☐
15 - 9 = ☐
13 - 4 = ☐

Score ☐

18 - 6 = ☐
14 - 5 = ☐
19 - 8 = ☐
12 - 3 = ☐
17 - 7 = ☐
15 - 8 = ☐
13 - 9 = ☐
11 - 4 = ☐
16 - 1 = ☐
12 - 8 = ☐

Score ☐

For answers see page 31

Addition and subtraction facts up to 20

6 + 8 = ☐	18 - 5 = ☐	6 + 8 = ☐
12 - 7 = ☐	7 + 9 = ☐	15 - 6 = ☐
5 + 9 = ☐	14 - 2 = ☐	5 + 3 = ☐
13 - 5 = ☐	4 + 5 = ☐	17 - 4 = ☐
4 + 7 = ☐	10 - 7 = ☐	7 + 9 = ☐
16 - 4 = ☐	6 + 8 = ☐	12 - 6 = ☐
8 + 7 = ☐	15 - 1 = ☐	8 + 7 = ☐
15 - 6 = ☐	9 + 6 = ☐	16 - 5 = ☐
6 + 2 = ☐	18 - 7 = ☐	6 + 4 = ☐
17 - 3 = ☐	7 + 3 = ☐	19 - 5 = ☐

Score

Score

Score

For answers see page 31

Doubles of numbers up to 10

5 + 5 = ☐

2 + 2 = ☐

6 + 6 = ☐

1 + 1 = ☐

3 + 3 = ☐

7 + 7 = ☐

4 + 4 = ☐

8 + 8 = ☐

10 + 10 = ☐

9 + 9 = ☐

Score ☐

2 + 2 = ☐

5 + 5 = ☐

4 + 4 = ☐

1 + 1 = ☐

7 + 7 = ☐

3 + 3 = ☐

8 + 8 = ☐

10 + 10 = ☐

6 + 6 = ☐

9 + 9 = ☐

Score ☐

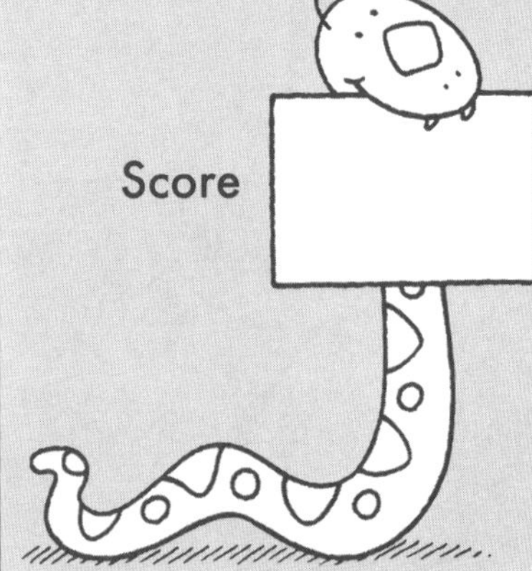

3 + 3 = ☐

6 + 6 = ☐

1 + 1 = ☐

8 + 8 = ☐

4 + 4 = ☐

10 + 10 = ☐

2 + 2 = ☐

5 + 5 = ☐

7 + 7 = ☐

9 + 9 = ☐

Score ☐

For answers see page 31

Missing numbers in addition up to 10

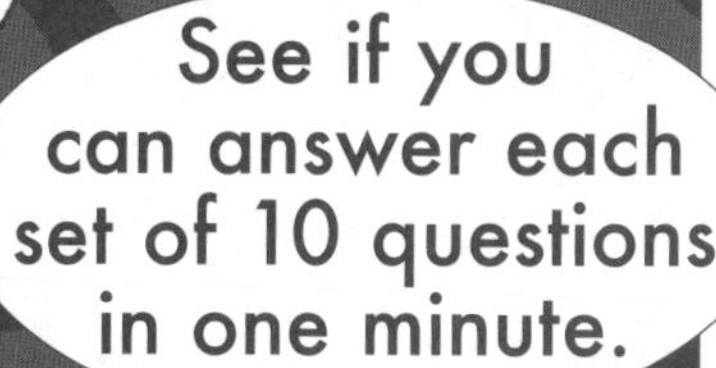

4 + ☐ = 6	1 + ☐ = 3	1 + ☐ = 4
2 + ☐ = 5	5 + ☐ = 7	2 + ☐ = 5
3 + ☐ = 7	2 + ☐ = 8	5 + ☐ = 7
5 + ☐ = 8	4 + ☐ = 5	3 + ☐ = 8
2 + ☐ = 4	1 + ☐ = 6	6 + ☐ = 8
1 + ☐ = 5	3 + ☐ = 5	4 + ☐ = 7
3 + ☐ = 6	2 + ☐ = 7	7 + ☐ = 9
4 + ☐ = 7	4 + ☐ = 8	2 + ☐ = 3
2 + ☐ = 6	5 + ☐ = 6	5 + ☐ = 9
3 + ☐ = 4	3 + ☐ = 9	1 + ☐ = 7

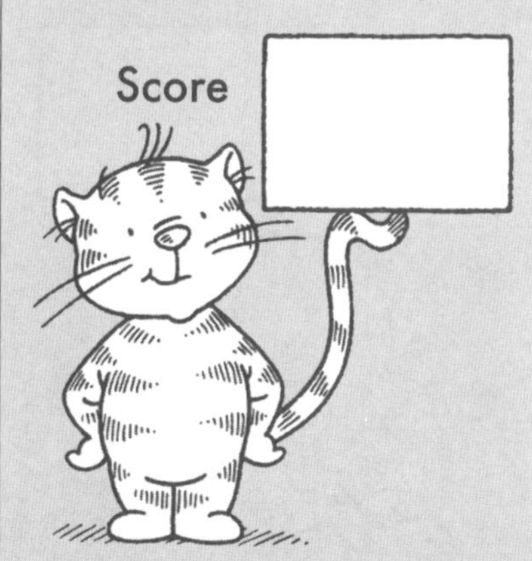

For answers see page 31

Missing numbers in subtraction up to 10

See if you can answer each set of 10 questions in one minute.

7 - ☐ = 3	7 - ☐ = 5	8 - ☐ = 5
8 - ☐ = 2	5 - ☐ = 3	6 - ☐ = 4
5 - ☐ = 4	6 - ☐ = 1	4 - ☐ = 1
9 - ☐ = 7	7 - ☐ = 2	9 - ☐ = 2
3 - ☐ = 1	9 - ☐ = 5	8 - ☐ = 3
6 - ☐ = 5	3 - ☐ = 2	5 - ☐ = 2
9 - ☐ = 3	8 - ☐ = 4	6 - ☐ = 3
7 - ☐ = 1	4 - ☐ = 3	5 - ☐ = 1
8 - ☐ = 6	6 - ☐ = 2	4 - ☐ = 2
7 - ☐ = 4	5 - ☐ = 1	9 - ☐ = 4

Score

Score

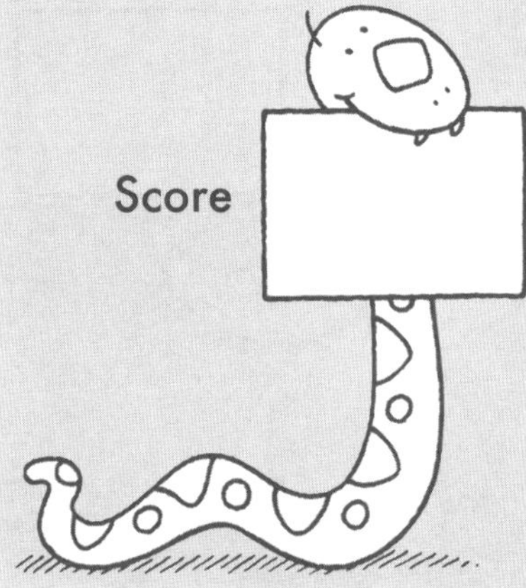

Score

For answers see page 32

Missing numbers in addition and subtraction up to 10

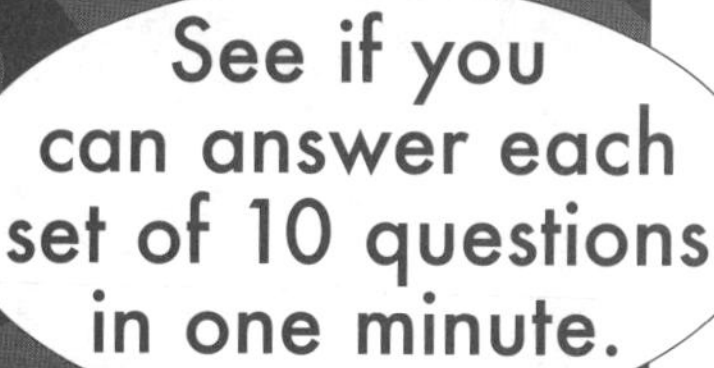

4 + ___ = 8	5 + ___ = 7	5 + ___ = 8
6 - ___ = 4	6 - ___ = 1	6 - ___ = 2
5 + ___ = 9	3 + ___ = 6	3 + ___ = 5
8 - ___ = 2	5 - ___ = 3	9 - ___ = 4
2 + ___ = 6	7 + ___ = 9	4 + ___ = 9
7 - ___ = 5	4 - ___ = 1	4 - ___ = 1
4 + ___ = 6	2 + ___ = 5	1 + ___ = 8
6 - ___ = 3	8 - ___ = 5	7 - ___ = 3
3 + ___ = 8	1 + ___ = 6	4 + ___ = 7
8 - ___ = 6	7 - ___ = 3	8 - ___ = 5

Score

Score

Score

For answers see page 32

Missing numbers in addition up to 20

See if you can answer each set of 10 questions in one minute.

12 + ☐ = 17
13 + ☐ = 19
11 + ☐ = 17
12 + ☐ = 13
13 + ☐ = 14
12 + ☐ = 18
14 + ☐ = 15
11 + ☐ = 16
13 + ☐ = 16
14 + ☐ = 17

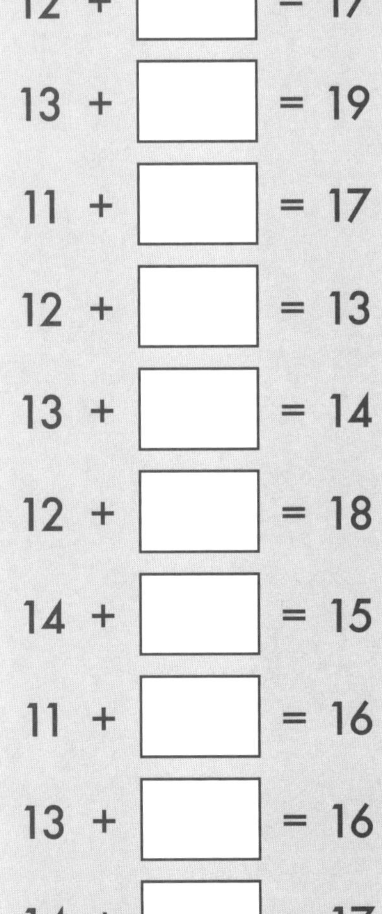

11 + ☐ = 13
13 + ☐ = 15
12 + ☐ = 17
15 + ☐ = 17
13 + ☐ = 18
15 + ☐ = 18
12 + ☐ = 14
11 + ☐ = 15
15 + ☐ = 17
12 + ☐ = 16

16 + ☐ = 18
14 + ☐ = 17
17 + ☐ = 19
14 + ☐ = 18
15 + ☐ = 16
12 + ☐ = 15
13 + ☐ = 17
11 + ☐ = 14
15 + ☐ = 19
12 + ☐ = 15

For answers see page 32

Missing numbers in subtraction up to 20

See if you can answer each set of 10 questions in one minute.

18 - ☐ = 13
16 - ☐ = 14
14 - ☐ = 11
15 - ☐ = 13
18 - ☐ = 14
14 - ☐ = 13
16 - ☐ = 12
19 - ☐ = 13
17 - ☐ = 14
18 - ☐ = 13

Score ☐

18 - ☐ = 12
16 - ☐ = 15
19 - ☐ = 15
13 - ☐ = 12
16 - ☐ = 11
17 - ☐ = 12
19 - ☐ = 12
18 - ☐ = 13
15 - ☐ = 12
16 - ☐ = 13

Score ☐

15 - ☐ = 11
14 - ☐ = 12
17 - ☐ = 11
19 - ☐ = 17
13 - ☐ = 11
15 - ☐ = 11
18 - ☐ = 15
19 - ☐ = 14
15 - ☐ = 14
17 - ☐ = 13

Score ☐

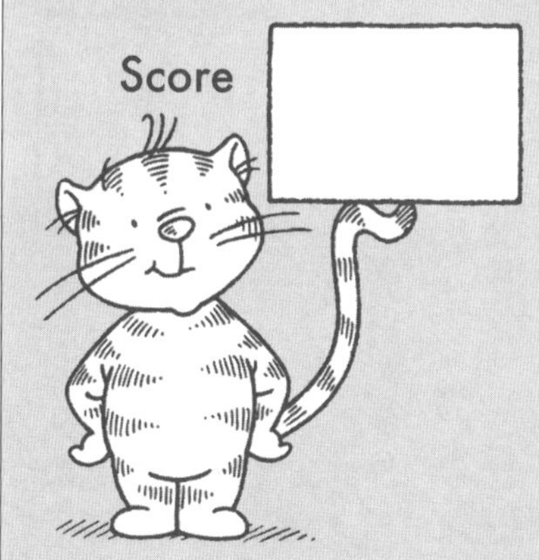

For answers see page 32

Missing numbers in addition and subtraction up to 20

11 + ☐ = 17	12 + ☐ = 13	15 + ☐ = 17
16 − ☐ = 15	15 − ☐ = 13	14 − ☐ = 13
13 + ☐ = 14	14 + ☐ = 18	13 + ☐ = 18
14 − ☐ = 11	14 − ☐ = 12	18 − ☐ = 13
14 + ☐ = 17	13 + ☐ = 15	13 + ☐ = 19
16 − ☐ = 11	13 − ☐ = 11	19 − ☐ = 12
15 + ☐ = 16	17 + ☐ = 19	13 + ☐ = 17
19 − ☐ = 13	18 − ☐ = 13	18 − ☐ = 15
12 + ☐ = 15	12 + ☐ = 17	11 + ☐ = 14
19 − ☐ = 15	17 − ☐ = 11	15 − ☐ = 14

Score ☐

Score ☐

Score ☐

For answers see page 32

Adding one-digit numbers to two-digit numbers

See if you can answer each set of 10 questions in one minute.

23 + 4 =	31 + 8 =	37 + 2 =
41 + 7 =	54 + 4 =	62 + 7 =
35 + 2 =	63 + 5 =	26 + 3 =
13 + 5 =	28 + 1 =	13 + 4 =
20 + 9 =	73 + 4 =	42 + 6 =
32 + 7 =	24 + 3 =	53 + 5 =
17 + 2 =	15 + 2 =	74 + 3 =
46 + 3 =	34 + 4 =	82 + 7 =
52 + 5 =	50 + 7 =	61 + 5 =
18 + 1 =	45 + 3 =	44 + 4 =

Score

Score

Score

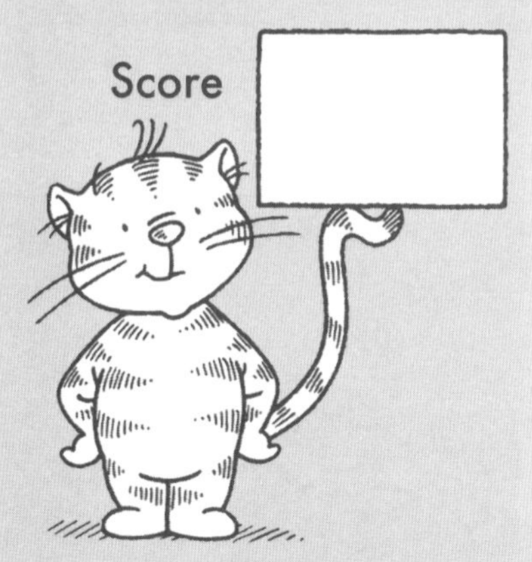

For answers see page 32

More addition of one-digit numbers to two-digit numbers

See if you can answer each set of 10 questions in one minute.

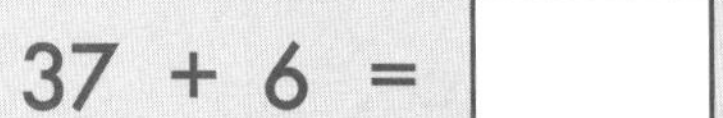

37 + 6 = ☐	58 + 4 = ☐	58 + 4 = ☐
52 + 8 = ☐	26 + 5 = ☐	67 + 7 = ☐
31 + 6 = ☐	39 + 7 = ☐	44 + 9 = ☐
64 + 7 = ☐	41 + 6 = ☐	85 + 5 = ☐
15 + 5 = ☐	84 + 8 = ☐	27 + 6 = ☐
66 + 5 = ☐	18 + 4 = ☐	36 + 7 = ☐
47 + 4 = ☐	73 + 9 = ☐	19 + 3 = ☐
56 + 2 = ☐	25 + 7 = ☐	28 + 5 = ☐
29 + 3 = ☐	53 + 8 = ☐	76 + 8 = ☐
34 + 7 = ☐	48 + 3 = ☐	86 + 7 = ☐

Score ☐

Score ☐

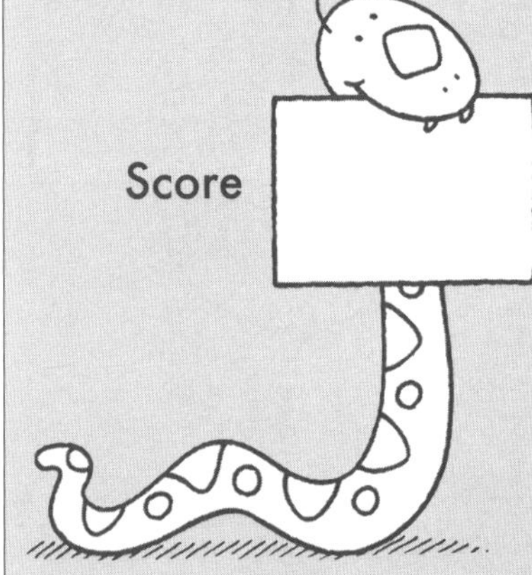

Score ☐

For answers see page 32

Subtracting one-digit numbers from two-digit numbers

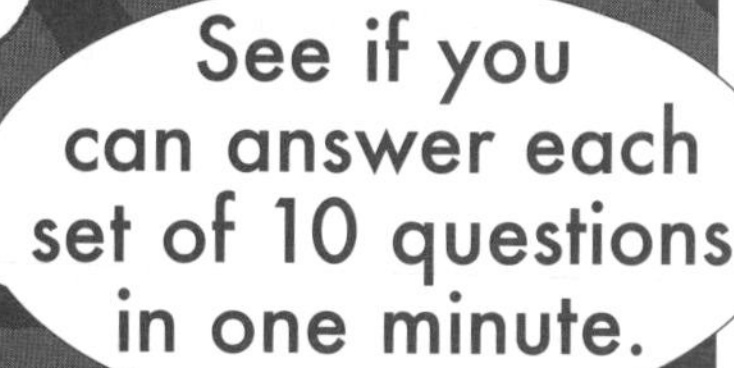
See if you can answer each set of 10 questions in one minute.

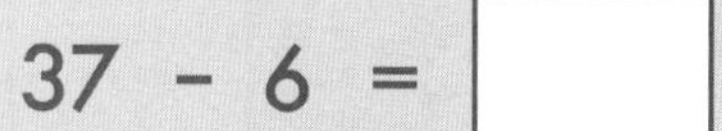

37 - 6 = ☐

28 - 2 = ☐

54 - 3 = ☐

67 - 5 = ☐

18 - 7 = ☐

45 - 3 = ☐

76 - 4 = ☐

68 - 3 = ☐

38 - 5 = ☐

27 - 4 = ☐

Score

59 - 6 = ☐

37 - 4 = ☐

89 - 7 = ☐

25 - 4 = ☐

76 - 2 = ☐

58 - 3 = ☐

49 - 7 = ☐

68 - 8 = ☐

96 - 3 = ☐

74 - 2 = ☐

Score

38 - 6 = ☐

46 - 3 = ☐

27 - 4 = ☐

19 - 6 = ☐

58 - 6 = ☐

26 - 5 = ☐

18 - 2 = ☐

67 - 5 = ☐

79 - 7 = ☐

87 - 3 = ☐

Score

For answers see page 32

Mental maths mixture

See if you can answer each set of 10 questions in one minute.

5 + 1 = ☐	4 + 5 = ☐	5 + ☐ = 18
7 + 1 = ☐	6 - 4 = ☐	8 - ☐ = 3
15 + 1 = ☐	6 + 6 = ☐	2 + ☐ = 9
8 - 1 = ☐	8 - 3 = ☐	6 - ☐ = 1
12 + 1 = ☐	7 - 5 = ☐	12 + ☐ = 19
15 - 1 = ☐	10 - 7 = ☐	19 - ☐ = 14
54 + 1 = ☐	10 - 4 = ☐	13 + ☐ = 17
76 + 1 = ☐	5 + 8 = ☐	73 + 6 = ☐
28 - 1 = ☐	18 - 6 = ☐	56 + 8 = ☐
45 - 1 = ☐	7 + 7 = ☐	78 - 5 = ☐
Score ☐	Score ☐	Score ☐

For answers see page 32

Page 3 Adding 1 to numbers up to 10

Column 1	Column 2	Column 3
5	6	8
8	3	1
3	8	2
6	7	7
1	2	4
10	4	9
7	9	5
2	5	10
9	1	3
4	10	6

Page 4 Subtracting 1 from numbers up to 10

Column 1	Column 2	Column 3
6	2	9
3	6	4
8	0	1
5	4	6
4	7	7
1	9	2
9	3	5
2	5	0
0	1	3
7	8	8

Page 5 Adding and subtracting 1 from numbers up to 10

Column 1	Column 2	Column 3
6	3	7
5	4	2
4	5	9
2	7	3
9	7	2
7	2	8
1	2	6
5	6	5
6	6	3
10	8	6

Page 6 Adding 1 to numbers up to 20

Column 1	Column 2	Column 3
13	18	11
17	15	16
16	17	18
20	20	14
11	9	19
14	16	8
18	12	13
10	14	17
15	19	12
12	13	15

Page 7 Subtracting 1 from numbers up to 20

Column 1	Column 2	Column 3
13	17	12
16	13	16
9	16	11
14	10	18
18	15	10
11	18	9
17	9	13
15	19	17
12	11	19
10	14	14

Page 8 Adding and subtracting 1 up to 20

Column 1	Column 2	Column 3
14	13	17
14	14	16
19	18	14
11	12	18
15	16	11
18	16	11
18	11	16
9	17	10
17	17	19
10	11	13

Page 9 Adding 1 to numbers up to 100

Column 1	Column 2	Column 3
40	63	76
66	30	50
43	85	33
82	31	97
59	79	22
61	53	66
75	46	58
23	74	90
38	99	37
52	84	52

Page 10 Subtracting 1 from numbers up to 100

Column 1	Column 2	Column 3
59	44	55
34	51	93
77	92	19
21	70	44
48	29	36
82	88	64
53	43	72
91	27	28
33	65	87
78	86	69

Page 11 Adding and subtracting 1 up to 100

Column 1	Column 2	Column 3
84	46	72
77	81	28
22	65	58
55	24	39
36	72	85
83	82	61
97	96	20
42	90	35
9	37	94
70	55	53

Page 12
Addition facts up to 10

Column 1	Column 2	Column 3
9	8	9
10	8	10
5	7	8
7	9	10
8	10	10
9	9	9
9	8	7
6	6	7
9	7	10
7	10	7

Page 13
Subtraction facts up to 10

Column 1	Column 2	Column 3
5	2	3
3	5	0
5	4	1
2	0	1
2	1	4
3	1	1
2	3	2
1	1	1
1	3	4
3	0	2

Page 14
Addition and subtraction facts up to 10

Column 1	Column 2	Column 3
8	2	7
2	9	3
8	4	8
1	9	2
10	2	10
0	7	1
8	2	9
2	7	0
9	1	9
2	10	2

Page 15
Subtracting from 10

Column 1	Column 2	Column 3
6	2	7
5	7	3
7	5	8
2	9	4
9	6	5
3	1	2
8	4	6
7	3	9
4	8	1
1	2	3

Page 16
Addition facts up to 20

Column 1	Column 2	Column 3
15	8	14
12	13	11
10	11	9
11	14	11
14	8	14
8	10	11
9	16	11
9	11	13
13	12	13
15	7	14

Page 17
Subtraction facts up to 20

Column 1	Column 2	Column 3
7	12	12
13	6	9
7	16	11
6	8	9
13	14	10
15	11	7
10	6	4
12	9	7
5	6	15
6	9	4

Page 18
Addition and subtraction facts up to 20

Column 1	Column 2	Column 3
14	13	14
5	16	9
14	12	8
8	9	13
11	3	16
12	14	6
15	14	15
9	15	11
8	11	10
14	10	14

Page 19
Doubles of numbers up to 10

Column 1	Column 2	Column 3
10	4	6
4	10	12
12	8	2
2	2	16
6	14	8
14	6	20
8	16	4
16	20	10
20	12	14
18	18	18

Page 20
Missing numbers in addition up to 10

Column 1	Column 2	Column 3
2	2	3
3	2	3
4	6	2
3	1	5
2	5	2
4	2	3
3	5	2
3	4	1
4	1	4
1	6	6

Page 21
Missing numbers in subtraction up to 10

Column 1	Column 2	Column 3
4	2	3
6	2	2
1	5	3
2	5	7
2	4	5
1	1	3
6	4	3
6	1	4
2	4	2
3	4	5

Page 22
Missing numbers in addition and subtraction up to 10

Column 1	Column 2	Column 3
4	2	3
2	5	4
4	3	2
6	2	5
4	2	5
2	3	3
2	3	7
3	3	4
5	5	3
2	4	3

Page 23
Missing numbers in addition up to 20

Column 1	Column 2	Column 3
5	2	2
6	2	3
6	5	2
1	2	4
1	5	1
6	3	3
1	2	4
5	4	3
3	2	4
3	4	3

Page 24
Missing numbers in subtraction up to 20

Column 1	Column 2	Column 3
5	6	4
2	1	2
3	4	6
2	1	2
4	5	2
1	5	4
4	7	3
6	5	5
3	3	1
5	3	4

Page 25
Missing numbers in addition and subtraction up to 20

Column 1	Column 2	Column 3
6	1	2
1	2	1
1	4	5
3	2	5
3	2	6
5	2	7
1	2	4
6	5	3
3	5	3
4	6	1

Page 26
Adding one-digit numbers to two-digit numbers

Column 1	Column 2	Column 3
27	39	39
48	58	69
37	68	29
18	29	17
29	77	48
39	27	58
19	17	77
49	38	89
57	57	66
19	48	48

Page 27
More addition of one-digit numbers to two-digit numbers

Column 1	Column 2	Column 3
43	62	62
60	31	74
37	46	53
71	47	90
20	92	33
71	22	43
51	82	22
58	32	33
32	61	84
41	51	93

Page 28
Subtracting one-digit numbers from two-digit numbers

Column 1	Column 2	Column 3
31	53	32
26	33	43
51	82	23
62	21	13
11	74	52
42	55	21
72	42	16
65	60	62
33	93	72
23	72	84

Page 29
Mental maths mixture

Column 1	Column 2	Column 3
6	9	13
8	2	5
16	12	7
7	5	5
13	2	7
14	3	5
55	6	4
77	13	79
27	12	64
44	14	73